Giuseppe and Josephine Nesci, 1965
This book is dedicated to honor the enduring love of all grandparents
for their grandchildren wherever they are.

4591 Ben Hur Road
Mariposa, CA 95338

The story "Grandma's & Grandpa's The Rainbow Covenant"
is an imprint of Nesci Publishing Co.
Published by Nesci Publishing Co.
4591 Ben Hur Road
Mariposa, CA 95338
Copyright © 2013 Giuseppe & Josephine Nesci
Mariposa, California
All rights reserved.
Printed in Hong Kong
10 9 8 7 6 5 4 3 2 1

Library of Congress Control Number: 2013938403
Giuseppe & Josephine Nesci
The story of "Grandma's & Grandpa's The Rainbow Covenant" by Giuseppe & Josephine Nesci
Illustrated by Ernie "Hergie" Hergenroeder
Summary: The story of three grandchildren and their experience of seeing
and learning about the rainbow and God's promise as explained by Grandma.
ISBN: 978-0-9892313-0-5 (Hardcover)
Copyright to include all characters, design & story concept.

Once upon a time in a small mountain town on a rainy day, Ashley, Shelby and Spencer were visiting their grandparents. The rain had stopped, and they were playing outdoors.

Ashley looked up into the sky and saw the most beautiful rainbow.
"Grandma", shouted Ashley, "look at that rainbow in the sky!"

"Yes, that is a rainbow; isn't it pretty? Come in the house
and I will tell you a story about the rainbow," said Grandma.
"I have some fresh baked gingerbread cookies for you."

"Be careful Spencer, the cookies are still hot from the oven.
We'll let them cool for just a little while and I will pour
you some milk to have with the cookies."

"Grandma, look at the rainbow shining through the angel!"
"Yes, Grandma, rainbows are everywhere! They're all over the
walls too! Cookies, milk and rainbows, WOW,
Grandma, you have everything!"

5

"OK children, let's learn about rainbows."
Grandma took her Bible off the table and opened it to
the story of Noah's Ark. Grandma then sat down in her
rocking chair and began to read the story.

"This is what the Bible says about the rainbow and God's covenant..."

"I establish my covenant with you: never again will all life be cut off by the waters of a flood; never again will a flood destroy the earth. As a sign of His covenant with man, God placed a rainbow in the clouds. Whenever a rainbow appears in the clouds to this very day, it is a sign of God's faithful promise and His memory of it."

Genises 9: 11-17

7

"Spencer, a covenant is a promise.
It's like the promise you made to take care of Tuffy, your puppy;
you love him and feed him. Tuffy depends on you to feed
him. That is why he is wagging his tail to say thank you."

8

"It is a wonderful promise to care for all of us and all the animals of the earth. Every time you look up into the sky and see a rainbow, it is a reminder that God is still here and is looking over ALL OF US."

9

"The farmer cares and feeds all of his farm animals. His cows, pigs, horses, sheep and chickens all need him for their survival. They are domestic animals and are important to the farmer because they give him back many products."

"Wild animals are different from farm animals. God provides for the wild animals on the earth and has placed a special instinct into them. They are born with an ability of how to survive.

"Squirrels know to gather and save acorns all summer
long so they will have food to eat during the winter
when trees are not producing acorns."

"The big, brown Bear sleeps (hibernates) during the cold,
long winter months. Then in the early spring when new berries
and grass begin to grow and the snow begins to melt,
the bear comes out of her den to eat."

13

"When summer's end approaches, you can see many kinds of birds flying south to a warmer climate where food is more plentiful and the weather is less harsh."

"Even the fish and animals of the ocean migrate to other regions of the sea to find new food sources and to give birth to babies."

WINTER

SPRING

SUMMER

AUTUMN

"The trees and flowers also are affected by the seasons. In the cold winter, many trees lose their leaves and stop producing fruit. The bushes and grasses also stop growing. Then in the spring they all come alive with new growth. You can even smell it in the air."

"Every year is the same; in the winter you get to play in snow, and in summer you can swim in the lake. You can trust the Rainbow Covenant just like the changing seasons."

Later that evening it was time for bed. The children put on their jammies and brushed their teeth. Grandma came into the bedroom to tuck them into bed and say goodnight prayers.

"Goodnight my angels, it's time to dream of rainbows and gingerbread cookies," said Grandma. The children all said, "Goodnight Grandma, we love you."

19

And the dreams of rainbows, gingerbread cookies, and Grandmas love will continue from seasons to seasons and years to come.

Gingerbread Cookies

INGREDIENTS:

1 cup butter
1 cup sugar
1 tablespoon ginger
2 teaspoons cinnamon
1 teaspoon cloves
1/2 cup water
1/2 cup dark corn syrup
4 cups all purpose flour
1-1/2 teaspoons baking soda
1/4 teaspoon salt

DIRECTIONS:

Combine sugar, spices, water, and corn syrup in a small pan. Bring to a boil while stirring constantly. Remove from heat and pour over butter in large mixing bowl. Stir until butter melts; cool to luke warm. Combine flour, baking soda and salt. Add in butter mixture; mix well. Cover and refrigerate dough overnight. Preheat your oven to 375 degrees F. Roll the dough on a lightly floured surface to 1/8 inch thickness. Cut with floured cookie cutter. Bake on unbuttered cookie sheet for 12 to 15 minutes. Cool completely on a wire rack. Decorate.
Makes 3 dozen 6 inch cookies.